# The Boosey & Hawkes
# Solo Piano Collection

## BEST OF BRITISH

### 29 British gems arranged for the intermediate pianist

selected by Hywel Davies

Boosey & Hawkes Music Publishers Ltd
www.boosey.com

# ARRANGER BIOGRAPHIES

HYWEL DAVIES

Hywel Davies was born and brought up in London. He is active as a creative artist, editor and arranger. An award-winning composer, Davies has a long-standing association with Kokoro (Bournemouth Symphony Orchestra's new music ensemble) and other musicians and ensembles across Europe and North America; he was also the recipient of an Arts Council England International Fellowship in 2003. As a sonic and installation artist he has created works for Arts Council England's internal phone system, the former USAF base at Greenham Common and a ringtone to mark the handover of the Olympic flag from Beijing to London. His work as an arranger has been published by Boosey & Hawkes, Durand-Salabert-Eschig, Chester Music, Novello, the Associated Board of the Royal Schools of Music and Music Sales. For Boosey & Hawkes his arrangements include two volumes of pieces by Astor Piazzolla and a volume of works by Rachmaninoff; he has also compiled four anthologies of piano music for them — *Animations*, *Contemplations*, *Fascinations* and *Gradations*.

www.hyweldavies.co.uk

CHRISTOPHER NORTON

Christopher Norton was born in New Zealand in 1953. After graduating he began his career as a teacher, pianist and composer, and began to develop an interest in popular music. Coming to the UK in 1977 on a university scholarship, he studied composition at York University with Wilfred Mellers and David Blake. Well established as a composer, producer, arranger and educationalist, Norton has written stage musicals, ballet scores, piano music, popular songs and orchestral music as well as jingles and signature tunes for TV and radio. He has lectured all over the world on aspects of his work and likes to integrate traditional teaching methods with aspects of modern technology. Chris is best known for his world-famous series *Microjazz* — easy graded pieces in modern styles such as blues, rock 'n' roll, reggae and jazz — and for his award-winning *Essential Guides to Pop Styles*, *Latin Styles* and *Jazz Styles*.

www.christophernorton.com

Published by Boosey & Hawkes Music Publishers Ltd
Aldwych House
71–91 Aldwych
London
WC2B 4HN

www.boosey.com

ISMN 979-0-060-12388-7
ISBN 978-0-85162-653-6

This impression 2020

Printed by Halstan:
Halstan UK, 2–10 Plantation Road, Amersham, Bucks, HP6 6HJ. United Kingdom
Halstan DE, Weißliliengasse 4, 55116 Mainz. Germany

Music origination by Robin Hagues
Cover design by Fresh Lemon

# CONTENTS

# ALFRED
## Rule, Britannia!

THOMAS ARNE
(1710–1778)
arranged by Hywel Davies

# A COLOUR SYMPHONY
## Purple

ARTHUR BLISS
(1891–1975)
arranged by Hywel Davies

# A CEREMONY OF CAROLS
## Interlude

BENJAMIN BRITTEN
(1913–1976)
arranged by Hywel Davies

# A HYMN TO THE VIRGIN

BENJAMIN BRITTEN
(1913–1976)
arranged by Hywel Davies

# THE YOUNG PERSON'S GUIDE
# TO THE ORCHESTRA
## Theme

BENJAMIN BRITTEN
(1913–1976)
arranged by Christopher Norton

# PETER GRIMES
## Interlude V: Evening (Moonlight)

BENJAMIN BRITTEN
(1913–1976)
arranged by Hywel Davies

In the original version of this Interlude, Britten indicated that wherever the syncopated crotchet figure appears, there should be a gentle swell to every beat as demonstrated in this arrangement by the dyanamics in square brackets.

# A VILLAGE ROMEO AND JULIET
## The walk to the paradise garden

FREDERICK DELIUS
(1862–1934)
arranged by Christopher Norton

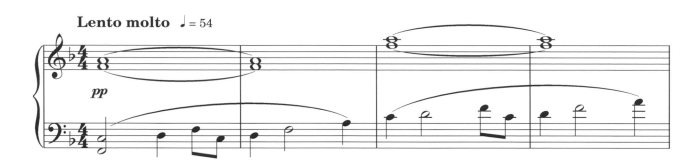

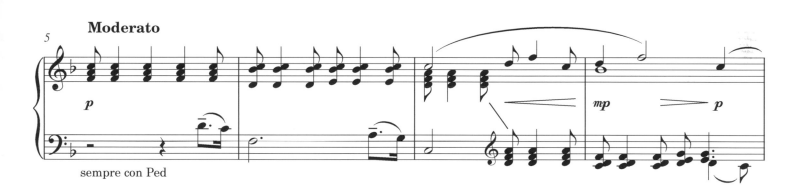

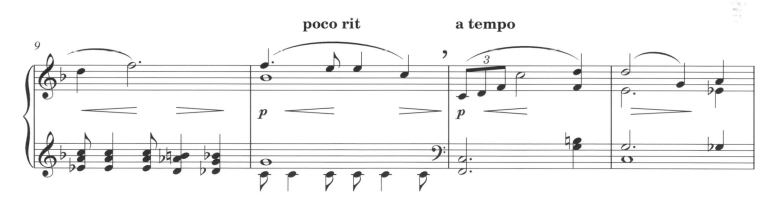

# MILITARY MARCHES 'POMP AND CIRCUMSTANCE'
## Land of hope and glory

EDWARD ELGAR
(1857-1934)
arranged by Hywel Davies

**Allegro con molto fuoco**

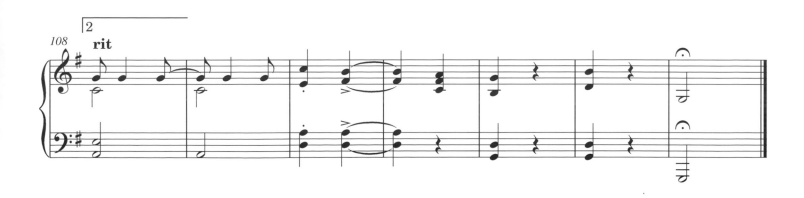

# VARIATIONS ON AN ORIGINAL THEME 'ENIGMA'
## Nimrod

EDWARD ELGAR
(1857–1934)
arranged by Christopher Norton

# CLARINET CONCERTO
## Theme from third movement

GERALD FINZI
(1901–1956)
arranged by Hywel Davies

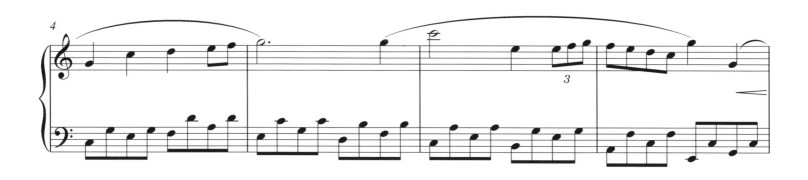

# ECLOGUE

GERALD FINZI
(1901–1956)
arranged by Hywel Davies

**ritard molto**                                    **a tempo, ma poch più movimento**

*cresc poco a poco*

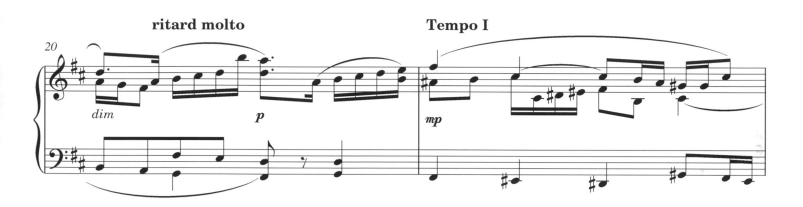

**ritard molto**  **Tempo I**

**ritard molto**

# FIVE BAGATELLES
## Romance

GERALD FINZI
(1901–1956)
arranged by Hywel Davies

**Andante tranquillo** ♩ = c84

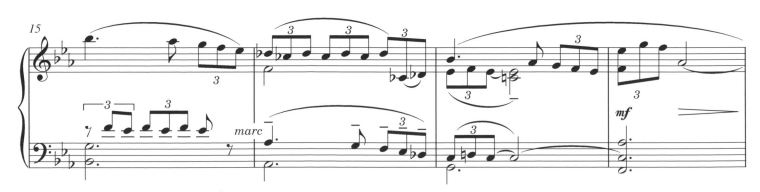

# FIVE BAGATELLES
## Prelude

GERALD FINZI
(1901–1956)
arranged by Hywel Davies

# THE PLANETS
## Jupiter

## I

GUSTAV HOLST
(1874–1934)
arranged by Christopher Norton

**Allegro giocoso** ♩ = 108

To Coda

*DC al Coda*

**CODA**

*Presto*

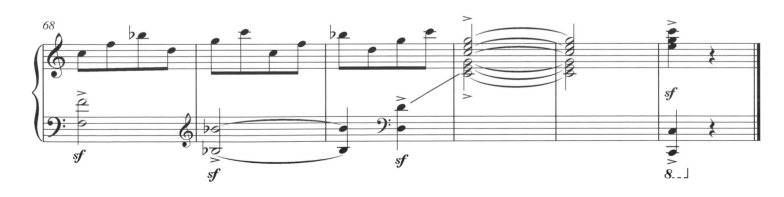

# II

**Andante maestoso**

**rall**

# THE PLANETS
## Venus

GUSTAV HOLST
(1874–1934)
arranged by Christopher Norton

★ The small notes may be omitted if desired.

# THE HOLY BOY

JOHN IRELAND
(1879–1962)
arranged by Christopher Norton

# A LONDON OVERTURE
## Theme

JOHN IRELAND
(1879–1962)
arranged by Hywel Davies

**Allegro brioso** ♩ = 84–88

# THE ARMED MAN
## Benedictus

KARL JENKINS
(b 1944)

# THE JOURNEY (THE BEST OF ADIEMUS)
## Cantilena

KARL JENKINS
(b 1944)

# PALLADIO
## Theme

KARL JENKINS
(b 1944)

*DS al Coda*

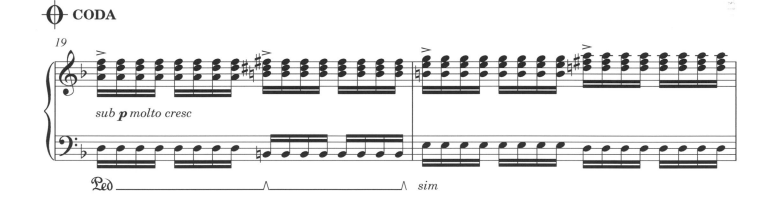

**CODA**

# SONGS OF SANCTUARY
## Adiemus

KARL JENKINS
(b 1944)
arranged by Hywel Davies

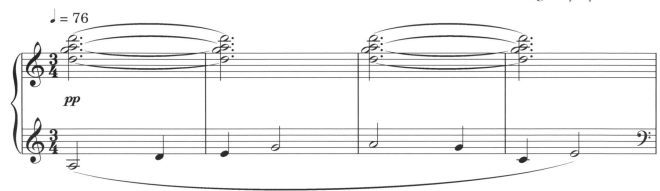

# THREE SCOTTISH SONGS

## Scots song

JAMES MACMILLAN
(b 1959)
arranged by Hywel Davies

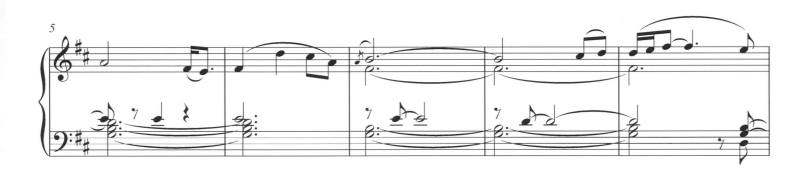

# NORTHERN SKIES
## Celtic hymn

JAMES MACMILLAN
(b 1959)
arranged by Hywel Davies

★ Acciaccaturas always played on the beat.

# FAREWELL TO STROMNESS

PETER MAXWELL DAVIES
(b 1934)

# AN ORKNEY WEDDING WITH SUNRISE
## Extract

PETER MAXWELL DAVIES
(b 1934)
arranged by Hywel Davies

# ENGLISH FOLK SONG SUITE

## March: Folk songs from Somerset

RALPH VAUGHAN WILLIAMS
(1872–1958)
arranged by Hywel Davies

# JERUSALEM

HUBERT PARRY
(1848–1918)
arranged by Hywel Davies

# MY NATIVE HEATH
## Barwick Green

ARTHUR WOOD
(1875–1953)

**Allegro giocoso (ma non troppo)**

# CAPRIOL SUITE
## Basse-danse

PETER WARLOCK
(1894–1930)
arranged by Christopher Norton

**Allegro moderato**